What they said about this I

Breath-taking in every respect. What a concept! And so beautifully rendered. In light of the global predicament we now face as in no other time throughout history, this tribute to Gandhi is at once a breath of fresh air and a stern reminder of what we must all do if sentience on this planet is to continue. We must delve deeply into our small selves to find the one true self and that each of us is a mirror looking out into a world of mirrors.

Christopher Herold

Such a wonderful concept, this conversation of a distinguished haiku master from Ireland with the Atma, the great soul the world knows as Gandhi, across times, cultures, and physical geographies. A truly moving text that pierces the heart and teaches it of love, of giving and receiving with worshipful reverence of life, of finding *mukti*, release, true liberty, in sharing, mutual consideration, and self-sacrifice.

Gracefully illustrated by Masood Hussain, the haunting third interlocutor, who puts his poignant images in colloquy with the haiku, the notes, sallies, and invitations to readers by the haiku master to join in the conversation, and through all these with the Maha Atma.

An illuminated, and illuminating, text for our times. A conference that in engaging us and seeking our participation unshackles in us a higher aspiration of living beyond self-serving and egotistical pretensions that wrack and convulse our world.

Waqas Khwaja

Walk with Gandhi

Bóthar na Saoirse

Haiku & Text:
Gabriel Rosenstock

Illustrations:
Masood Hussain

Foreword:
Ramachandra Guha

**Celebrating the 150th anniversary
of the Mahatma's birth
October 2, 1869 – October 2, 2019**

Nár dhéana an leabhar seo dochar d'éinne.
May this book harm no one.

People were much happier, Gandhi believed, when they lived simply, in small communities, and provided for their own needs, for example by spinning and weaving their own garments. Freedom, he hoped, would be accompanied by the dismantling of the mega-state and a return to the self-sufficient village of the past...

Ian Copland, *India 1885-1947: The Unmaking of an Empire*
(Pearson Education Limited, 2001)

First published in 2019 by
Gandhi 150 Ireland

© Gabriel Rosenstock 2019: Text and haiku in Irish (Gaelic) and English
© Masood Hussain 2019: Illustrations and artwork

Gabriel Rosenstock and Masood Hussain have asserted their moral right to be identified as the authors of this work in accordance with all relevant legislation.

British Library Cataloguing in Publication data
Rosentock, Gabriel
Walk with Gandhi
1. Mohandas K. Gandhi. 2. Haiku – Illustrations – History.
I. Title. II. Hussain, Masood.

Paperback: ISBN 978-1-9162254-0-4
Hardback: 978-1-9162254-2-8
Ebook: ISBN 978-1-9162254-1-1

Foreword

I was moved and enchanted by Gabriel Rosenstock's haiku on Gandhi. They run the range of human (and Mahatma-ic) emotions from sorrow to happiness, solemnity to mischief. They deserve, and will surely get, a wide readership across the world.

Ramachandra Guha, Author,
Gandhi: The Years That Changed The World **(Knopf 2019).**

Introduction

This bilingual book for young adults (and others) contains little vignettes, snapshots that give us an insight into the life and beliefs of Mohandas K. Gandhi, the 'great soul' we know today as the Mahatma. Look on these haiku as concentrated images that reflect the life and times of a remarkable man who freed India from the stranglehold and shackles of Empire.

Haiku cannot tell the whole story. All you will find here is a glimpse – an insight of such intensity that, hopefully, you will be inspired to find out more – about Gandhi, and about yourself!

The book you are holding in your hands was originally conceived as a work of photo-haiku, that is to say, haiku responding to actual historical photos of Mahatma Gandhi. Then we had the much better idea of asking a distinguished artist to come on board, Masood Hussain, and to re-interpret the photos in his own captivating style.

In turn, Masood's artwork inspired new haiku and the book took shape in this lively fashion, artwork and ideas flowing from Ireland to Kashmir and back again – via our project co-ordinator in New York. So, it's been around the world, you could say.

Acknowledgements

The creators of this book wish to thank a number of people who have provided invaluable assistance in bringing this project to fruition, including Rosheen Callender, Eithne Ní Chléirigh, Des Geraghty, Dr. Siby K. Joseph (Dean of Studies and Research, Institute of Gandhian Studies, Wardha, India) Rafiq Kathwari, Uma Magal, Yameema Mitha and Séamas Sheils. We also acknowledge the support of IMRAM – the Irish Language Literature Festival.

The photographic images used on pages 72 and 104 are both in the public domain.

caite amach as an traein...
caol díreach isteach san oíche
ionat féin

chucked out of the train...
into the dark night
of the soul

Well, what did you expect, Gandhi? You were in a "whites only" carriage in South Africa. You should have known your place, shouldn't you? Everyone should know his place!

This haiku alludes to a famous poem by St. John of the Cross, *La noche oscura del alma*. When we hear the phrase 'dark night of the soul', a spiritual crisis comes to mind. Getting himself thrown off the train was an awakening for Gandhi, a crisis you might say. In his lifelong quest for freedom and justice, he would bring millions of people along with him on a truly fantastic journey.

You gave us Mohandas; we returned him to you as Mahatma.
President Nelson Mandela in a speech in India

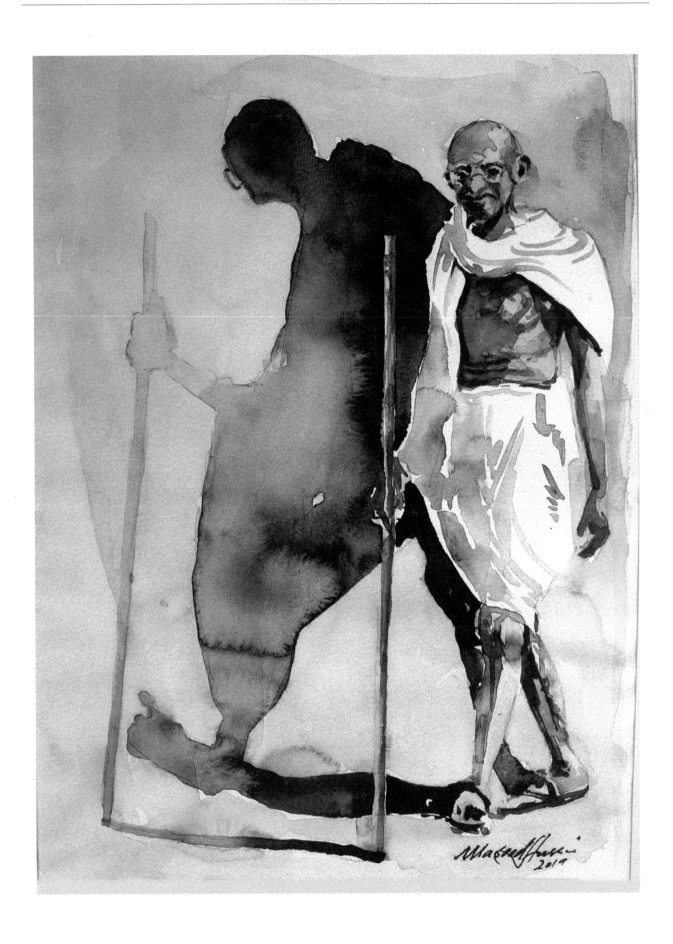

ligeann do scáil scíth
ach siúlann tusa ar aghaidh
go diongbháilte

your shadow rests
but you walk on
determined

! Even in his sixties, Gandhi walked at a brisk pace. He once believed that the English
had superiority over his fellow-Indians because they were stronger, being carnivores.
Most Hindus are vegetarians.

When studying law in London, Gandhi met many vegetarians and soon became
convinced that avoiding meat was the most ethical way to live. One way or the other, a
vegetarian diet didn't slow him down!

Find out more online, in print and film, about his stay in London and his many
adventures later as a young attorney in South Africa where he spent 21 years before his
return to India and the incredible destiny awaiting him.

a mhaide bheannaithe!
an tslí ar fad go Dandi
id' theannta

blessed staff!
with you all the way
to Dandi

Gandhiji's stick is now in a library in Vetapalem. He wanted a stick that was light so as not to harm insects and other little creatures on the road!

For many, he was like a return of Christ. For others, independent thinkers, Gandhi was a new incarnation of Jean-Jacques Rousseau and of Tolstoy, denouncing the illusions and the crimes of civilisation, and preaching to men the return to nature, to the simple life, to health.

Romain Rolland

is fada ag tnúth le do lámh iad...
gach gráinnín luachmhar
salainn

how they long for your hand...
each precious grain
of salt

One of the great events in India's freedom struggle was the march to Dandi, a coastal town in the Mahatma's native state, Gujarat. There he and his followers gathered sea-salt, a commodity which was taxed by the British administration. (India under British rule was known as the Raj. Direct rule lasted from 1859 to 1947, the year before Gandhi's death).

Gandhi marched from his ashram – a spiritual retreat – on March 12, 1930, and reached the shores of the Arabian Sea on April 5 where he and his followers helped themselves to some salt. It was a gesture that shook the Empire.

Gandhi and his followers had walked over 240 miles. Women and men were viciously clubbed when they reached Dandi; yet none of them offered any resistance as they fell, bleeding, to the ground.

The Mahatma believed that *ahimsa*, non-violence, was the key to emancipation, to personal and political freedom. Civil disobedience represented a moral force that would shame the British Empire in the eyes of the civilised world. Civil disobedience inspired other leaders, civil rights leaders in America and Northern Ireland, for instance, as well as many student groups such as OTPOR in Belgrade.

It is a tactic still used today by many people who campaign for various important issues, such as maintaining biodiversity, creating a clean and safe environment, advocating for peace, social justice and transparency and securing the survival of minority languages.

éanlaith na síthe
ag dul trí thine...
dubhaíonn is deargann spéartha

birds of peace
catch fire...
skies redden and darken

The Mahatma ('Great Soul') went on fasts whenever rioting broke out in India. It pained him greatly to see people being dominated by others, whether on the basis of caste – one's position in Hindu society – or religion. Yet there are many in India today who say he did not do enough to eradicate casteism or Varna. (Now some scholars say that casteism was not tradition-ally as virulent or divisive as we all thought it was: it came into its own as a result of the colonisers' interpretation of ancient texts).*

As a young man in South Africa, he once travelled first class on a train and was told that a sammy – slang for an Indian (based on the word *swami)* – had no right to travel first class. Gandhi insisted that he had every right and was thrown off the train. At that moment he said to himself, 'There's too much bullying in this world.' He would show, by example and by self-sacrifice, that turning the other cheek is an effective way to help the bully to realise his shameful ways.

He achieved much for the status of his fellow Indians in South Africa and learned strategies that he would employ on his return to India but native Africans – such as Zulus – do not hero-worship Gandhi today. Au contraire! Gandhi took the side of the British in the Zulu uprising of 1906. History is strange: full of contradictions.

Though Gandhi did nothing for native South Africans, concentrating his energy on the Indi-an minority there, he was an inspiration to Mandela and the African National Congress. Never-theless, students and professors in a university in Ghana were agitated by a statue of Gandhi. One night, the statue disappeared! Only the plinth remained.

Public statues can be controversial. For example, in University College, Cork, a statue of Queen Victoria was buried – the 'Famine Queen', 67 of whose regiments supervised the export of food from Ireland during the potato blight. Some very respectable people in Cork say it was a shame to bury her; she should be hauled out of the ground and cleaned up..

What do you think? Do you know what statues are in your area and who they commemorate? Is there someone who is neglected and who deserves a statue to her or his memory?

*Source: *Viewpoint: How the British reshaped India's caste system* by Sanjoy Chakravorty, Scroll.in., June 19, 2019.

tús troscaidh...
éiríonn giolc na n-éan
níos glóraí

the fast begins...
louder and louder
the chirping of birds

Fasting was often a form of personal penance for Gandhi, to atone, somehow, for failures or setbacks in his life-long campaign. Rightly or wrongly, he inspired others to use fasting as a political weapon.

In all, Gandhi undertook 17 fasts in the course of India's freedom struggle. These occurred in the years 1913, 1914, 1918, 1919, 1921, 1922, 1924, 1925 – twice in 1932 and 1933 – 1934, 1939, 1943, 1947, 1948.

The longest of these fasts lasted 21 days.

fan anois...
cén impireacht atá ag borradh
nó ag meath?

let's see...
what empire is on the rise
what empire wanes?

How many empires can you name?

How did they gain their strength and how did they collapse?

There are many reasons, of course. Empires often collapsed because they overextended – they literally went too far! Something as simple as poisonous lead in the water system may have contributed to the downfall of the Roman Empire. The British Empire was not the first empire to rule India. Before the British, there was the Mughal Empire. Everybody has their own theory about the collapse and who was to blame. One theory says it was all the fault of bankers.

By 1921, Gandhi was the leading figure in the Indian National Congress and changed it from being, mainly, a club for the Anglicised elite, mostly lawyers, into a beacon of hope for all.

He never lost an opportunity to preach *Swaraj,* in other words, complete independence from Britain. He believed that a boycott of British institutions – and goods – would speed them all on the road to freedom. Bonfires blazed, burning British clothes; and schools set up by the British were also boycotted.

The word boycott comes from Captain Charles Boycott who represented an absentee landlord, Lord Erne, in Co. Mayo. Captain Boycott was boycotted by the locals – even the postman refused to show up with the mail! Boycotting was famously used again in Ireland when oranges from South Africa were targeted in protest at the apartheid regime. It remains an important non-violent weapon today.

Do you know of any other campaigns where this tactic has been – or continues to be – used? How effective is the boycott as a weapon, compared to alternative forms of action?

tagann éanlaith strae
is éisteann le do chuid smaointe...
do thost

stray birds come
and listen to your thoughts...
your silence

! *Stray Birds* is the name of a slim volume of short prose-poems by Rabindranath
Tagore, a contemporary of Gandhi who was awarded the Nobel Prize for Literature.
It is said that he wrote it after a visit to Japan where he came under the influence of haiku.
It was Tagore, incidentally, who gave Gandhi the name Mahatma (Great Soul), four years
after his return to India, and Gandhi in return referred to Tagore as Gurudev (Supreme
Teacher).*

   Silence, too, is a great teacher and saying nothing at all is a form of fasting. In India,
silence is called *maun* or *moun*. We all talk too much! What is the longest period of silence
which you have ever observed?

   Gandhi said:

   *In the attitude of silence the soul finds the path in a clearer light, and what is elusive and
deceptive resolves itself into crystal clearness. Our life is a long and arduous quest after
Truth.*

In silence, we can get to know our own spirit and know that spirit is boundless. We have
nothing to fear. Gandhi helped others to overcome their fears. *Swaraj* was self-rule,
politically – and psychologically as well.

*Salmon Poetry published a bilingual edition of *Stray Birds* (in Irish and English)

gártha lúcháire
cé atá ann a chuimhneodh air?
...Críochdheighilt

cries of jubilation
who is there to remember?
...Partition

The partition of British India occurred in 1947. The refugee crisis led to death and suffering on an unimaginable scale and the creation of two new countries, Pakistan and India. (Later, in 1971, Bangladesh came into existence).

What do you know about the refugee problem today and its causes?
Would you like to see your country taking in more refugees?
Or are you a NIMBY (not in my back yard)?

gíoscán na gcairteacha daimh
níl aon deireadh leis...
an imirce mhór

creak of oxcarts
it never stops...
the great migration

 He was right, he knew he was right, we all knew he was right... 'Resist to the very end,' he said, 'but without violence.' Of violence the world is sick. Oh, India, dare to be worthy of your Gandhi.

Pearl S. Buck

cé atá in ann
croí duine eile a fheiscint
... a chroí féin

who can see
into the heart of another
...his own heart

On the advice of a mentor, Gopal Krishna Gokhale, (1866-1915), Gandhi spent almost two years reacquainting himself with his native land, before entering the political arena.

He took many train trips, always travelling third class in India, in an attempt to get to know the country and her people, a vast land with almost a thousand different languages. Like Christ, he preferred the poor and the workers to the idle rich and the speculators.

He never stopped questioning himself, his motives, his real or imagined weaknesses.

Can we ever know what's going on in someone else's mind?

What is really going on in your own mind, your own heart?

A great contemporary of Gandhi, Sri Ramana Maharshi, said that this is the most important question of all: who am I? Who is asking the question?

The Greeks, too, saw this as the beginning of philosophy: the unexamined life was a wasted life, according to Socrates.

You will face many tests and examinations in life but the most important one of all is self-examination.

Who are you? What are your values?

You might change your opinions but what is changeless and constant in you?

fórsaí ionraidh
ní athraíonn aon ní
ach an tuin chainte

invading forces
always the same...
only the accents change

 I believe that Gandhi's views were the most enlightened of all the political men in our time. We should strive to do things in his spirit: not to use violence in fighting for our cause, but by non-participation in anything you believe is evil.

Albert Einstein

ní leat féin ataoi...
 damhán alla, leis,
i gcarcair

not alone...
a spider shares
your prison cell

Who knows? He was imprisoned so often, there may well have been a spider in his cell. The spinning spider might have reminded him of the spinning wheel, a symbol of self-sufficiency, a political belief which he preached by example. Many thought he was naïve at the time but the notion of sustainability is on everybody's lips today.

Gandhi might have known of Robert the Bruce and how a spider inspired the Scotsman never to give up in his fight against English domination.

How many times was he imprisoned. Can you guess?

In South Africa he was imprisoned twice in 1908; then on February 25, 1909; November 6, 1913; November 7, 1913; November 9, 1913.

In India, he was arrested on April 16, 1917; April 10, 1919; jailed on March 10, 1922; May 5, 1930; January 4, 1932; August 1, 1933; August 4, 1933; August 9, 1942.

A bit of a trouble maker! But we are not obliged to obey unjust laws, are we?

Would you go to prison for your beliefs?

gairdín
in Amritsar...
deora fola ó na bláthanna

a garden
in Amritsar...
flowers weep blood

Reginald Dyer, a past pupil of Midleton College, Co. Cork, was the butcher in charge of the most infamous massacre in the history of the Raj. A Tipperary man, Michael O'Dwyer, then Lieutenant General of the Punjab, described the massacre as the "correct action" to take against a large crowd of unarmed civilians! Fifty soldiers kept firing, for over ten minutes, until they ran out of bullets leaving 379 dead and 1100 wounded.

Poet Sir Rabindranath Tagore returned the 'Sir' to the British after this barbaric incident.

(This haiku has a faint echo of a remark made by Irish poet, Charles Donnelly, who fought against Fascists in Spain: 'even the olives are bleeding'. He was shot on February 27, 1937, and they buried him under one of the olive trees to which he had alluded only a few days earlier).

Mahatma Gandhi came and stood at the door of India's destitute millions, clad as one of themselves, speaking to them in their own language ... who else has so unreservedly accepted the vast masses of the Indian people as his flesh and blood? ...Truth awakened Truth.

Rabindranath Tagore

táthar ag faire ort
gach cor asat...
cat i ndiaidh gealbhain

your every move
is watched...
a cat stalks a sparrow

Gandhi was loved by millions. Very often people couldn't hear a word he said but were happy to get a glimpse of him. He was despised as well, of course. The King-Emperor, Edward, couldn't stand him and told him that under no circumstances would he give up his Empire. His Empire?!

Gandhi had enemies at home as well, not just the secret service; Hindu nationalists believed strongly that he was too accommodating to Muslims. He survived six assassination attempts. A man by the name of Nathuram Godse didn't take any chances and shot the Mahatma three times. He had attempted to kill Gandhi before that. He considered that Gandhi had been too conciliatory towards Muslims when India was partitioned by the British in 1947.

You have your life ahead of you. Will you encourage the use of guns and armaments? Or will you help to spread a gospel of peace? Can one person make a difference?

Be the change you wish to see in the world, said Gandhi. Actually, he may never have said that though it's a popular saying which is attributed to him. But he did say: *"If we could change ourselves, the tendencies in the world would also change..."*

So, we have to work on ourselves first and then, by our example, the world will modify its habits and great changes can come about.

Have we any other choice than to hope and believe and by our own example to change the world for the better?

féach, féach!
fakir leathnocht ceannairceach
tagtha

look, look!
a half-naked seditious fakir
has come to town

This is how the 'Great Soul' was insultingly described by Winston Churchill. Churchill is regarded as a hero in Britain but not in India. A famine in the early 1940s wiped out three million people in Bengal. Churchill's policy of removal of food from the area was largely responsible for the holocaust.

[Source: The Guardian (March 29, 2019)]

The Mahatma was overwhelmed by the dire poverty he found all around him. There were many causes for this poverty. The chief was the policy of the British rulers who upset the balance between agriculture and industry in the villages, reduced India into being a purely raw material-producing country, and in the interests of British manufacture stifled her industrial growth. The result was that people who formerly carried on industrial pursuits in the villages were left idle...
Bharatan Kumarappa in Visva-Bharati Quarterly, October 2 1949

is fuaire iad ná gach príosún
inar caitheadh thú...
ráillí Shráid Downing

*colder than all the prisons
you've been thrown into...
Downing Street railings*

During his early years, as a student of law in London and as an attorney in South Africa, Gandhi had a certain admiration for Britain and British values. He was not alone. Denis Hurley, Catholic Archbishop of Durban, could see nothing wrong with British rule – until his eyes were opened. Did you know that the first concentration camps were built by the British in South Africa?

Gandhi's infatuation with Britishness would not last forever and one of the first things he did to divest himself of Western ways of thinking and behaving was to get rid of Western clothing.

Today, people are beginning to question the power that labels have and the dire conditions in which certain items of fashionable clothing are made. During Ireland's fight for political and cultural freedom, Douglas Hyde – later first President of Ireland – encouraged the use of the Irish kilt and was known to end his speeches on the subject with the rousing mantra, 'Down with trousers!'

A colonised people tend to mimic or admire almost everything about the coloniser. Changing his clothing was one way of 'decolonising' his mind and appearance.

Are there ways, other than changing your style of clothes, in which one can go about this process of decolonisation?

Jinnah
inis rún do chroí dúinn...
Jinnah, Athair an Náisiúin

Jinnah
what are you dreaming of...
Jinnah, Baba-i-Qaum

After Partition, Muhammad Ali Jinnah (1876-1948) was Governor General of Pakistan. In Urdu, he is often called *Quaid-i-Azam*, 'the great leader' or *Baba-i-Qaum*, 'father of the nation.'

In a brief biography that accompanied a collection of Jinnah's speeches and writings published in 1918, the Indian poet and independence activist, Sarojini Naidu, described him as follows:

Hindu by race and Muslim by religion – it may not be wholly idle to fancy something a little symbolic in the... parentage of a child destined to become "an Ambassador of the Hindu Muslim Unity."

Through non-violence, steadfast faith and strict adherence to rules of ethical conduct, Gandhi was able to achieve a level of statesmanship unparalleled in the history of human affairs.

Paula Marvelly, Editor, The Culturium

Vinoba. . .
tá do chroí chomh bocht
leis an deoir

Vinoba . . .
you have made your heart
as poor as a church-mouse

What kind of followers did Gandhi have? One of them was Vinoba Bhave who continued Gandhi's work after the Mahatma's assassination.

Writing on October 20, 1940, Gandhi introduced his readers to this mighty soul, the first person with whom Gandhi discussed his plans for civil disobedience:

He is an undergraduate having left college after my return to India in 1916. He is a Sanskrit scholar. He joined the Ashram almost at its inception. He was among the first members. In order to better qualify himself he took one year's leave to prosecute further studies in Sanskrit. And practically at the same hour at which he had left the Ashram a year before, he walked into it without notice. I had forgotten that he was due to arrive that day. He has taken part in every menial activity of the Ashram from scavenging to cooking.

Though he has a marvellous memory and is a student by nature, he has devoted the largest part of his time to spinning in which he has specialised as very few have. He believes in universal spinning being the central activity which will remove the poverty in the villages and put life into their deadness... He has abolished every trace of untouchability from his heart. He believes in communal unity with the same passion that I have. In order to know the best mind of Islam, he gave one year to the study of the Quran in the original. He therefore learnt Arabic. He found this study necessary for cultivating a living contact with the Muslims in his neighbourhood...

Kasturba...
an miongháire é sin...
ab ea?

Kasturba...
is that a smile...
is it?

As was the custom, theirs was an arranged marriage. Kasturba and Gandhi were both starting their teenage years when they got married! In spite of bad health – chronic bronchitis – she was active in many freedom campaigns and frequently imprisoned.

I have the greatest admiration and respect for Mahatma Gandhi. He was a great human being with a deep understanding of human nature. He made every effort to encourage the full development of the positive aspects of the human potential.

Dalai Lama

á sea
tae Sasanach...
tá rud éigin ann

ah yes
English tea...
it has a certain je ne sais quoi

English tea?! Where in England does it grow?
Gandhi didn't approve of tea, labelling it as an intoxicant.

Actually, he was quite fond of the stuff but when someone pointed out to him that it looked like he couldn't do without it, Gandhi – ever the self-disciplinarian – chucked the habit.

Did he have any weakness at all? Yes, he loved a ripe mango. He also loved the mango tree and how it bows down under the weight of its fruits, exhorting us to be humble!

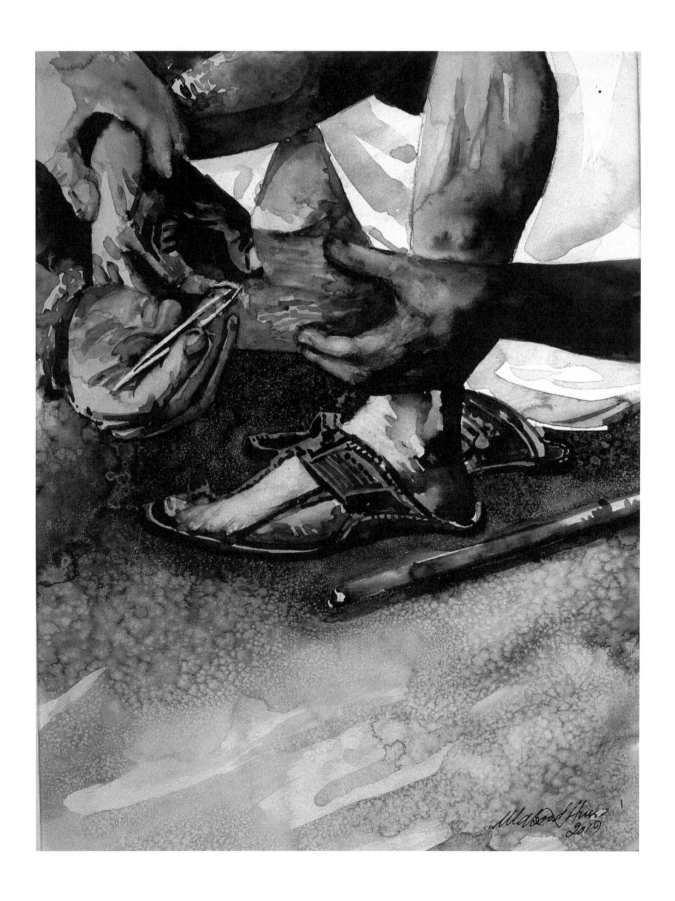

maolaigh pian an domhain...
baineann bearbóir dealg
as do chos

take away the world's pain...
a barber extracts
a thorn from your foot

This image was inspired by an actual photograph of a barber extracting a thorn from Gandhi's foot. Gandhi once spoke to students and shocked them by saying: "I consider that a barber's profession is just as good as the profession of medicine."*

Can the teachings or the life of any one individual – Christ, Buddha, Gandhi, Karl Marx, Mother Teresa – really change the world and reduce its suffering?

Who would you add to the list above? Who would you take from it?

* Quoted in *Mahatma Gandhi: Nonviolent Power in Action* by Dennis Dalton, Columbia University Press, 2012

an líne go dona...
a bhriathra ag cnagarnach
mar lasracha

the line is bad...
his words crackle
like flames

Don't say you don't have enough time or enough money to change the world. You have exactly the same number of hours per day that were given to Helen Keller, Gandhi, Michelangelo, Mother Teresa, Leonardo da Vinci and Jesus Christ.

Shannon L. Alder

sa charcair
ag cuimhneamh ar a póga...
Putlibai

in prison
remembering her kisses...
Putlibai

! Gandhi's mother, Putlibai, was very religious. Some of her rituals might sound strange
to us today. She would not touch food before seeing the Sun and saying a prayer. It is
said that as a child, Gandhi would often shout, excitedly, to her, 'Mother, come quickly!
The sun is out'; if it had disappeared behind rainclouds by the time she went outdoors,
Putlibai would go without food until its reappearance.

**Gandhi's whole political life of sacrifice and selfless service was for his
love of God, whom he longed to see until the very end!**

Meher Baba

cén t-athair
a shamhlódh é
a mhac féin – Athair an Náisiúin

what father
could imagine it
his own son – Father of the Nation

 Gandhi's father, Karamchand Uttamchand Gandhi (1822–1885) was a local politician in Gujarat.

> **Great men and eminent men have monuments in bronze and marble set up for them, but this man of divine fire managed in his lifetime to become enmeshed in millions and millions of hearts so that all of us have become somewhat of the stuff that he was made of, though to an infinitely lesser degree.**
>
> *Jawaharlal Nehru*

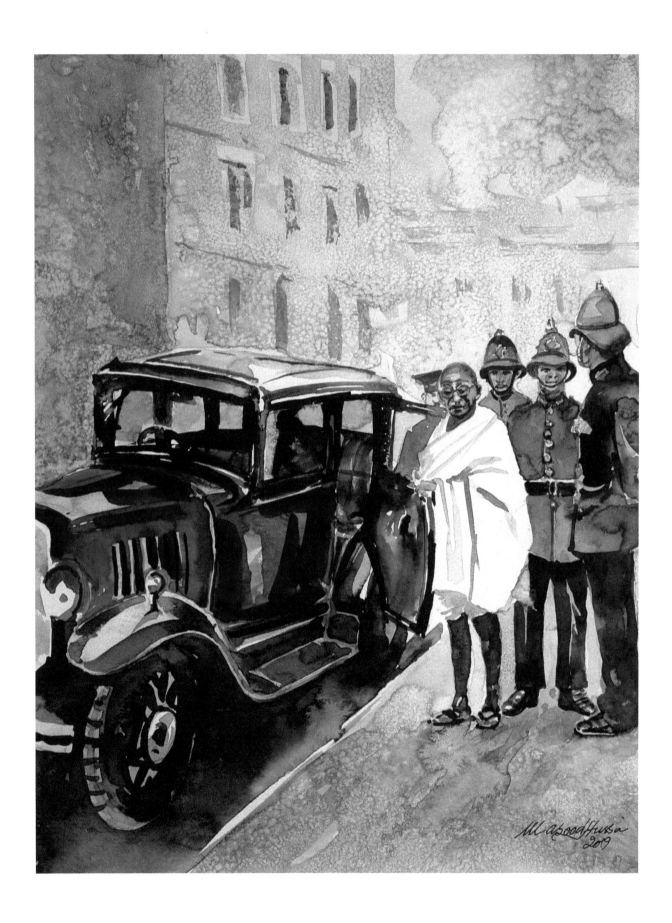

cnaipí snasta
clogaid socraithe...
póilíní ag déanamh iontais díot

buttons polished
helmets fixed...
policemen stare at you in wonder

If humanity is to progress, Gandhi is inescapable. He lived, thought, and acted, inspired by the vision of humanity evolving toward a world of peace and harmony. We may ignore him at our own risk.
Martin Luther King

sluaite ag iarraidh
spléachadh a fháil ort...
an féidir anam a fheiscint?

crowds gather
for a glimpse of you
who can see the soul?

! Gandhi did not like being called the Mahatma, a term that deified him. It comes from
the Sanskrit *mahā* meaning 'great' and *ātman* meaning 'soul'.

 **Don't ever forget, that we were not led by a saint with his head in the
clouds, but by a master tactician with his feet on the ground.**
Shashi Tharoor

Mohan mioscaiseach
ag casadh chluasa na ngadhar!
tháinig athrú ort

mischievous Mohan
twisting the ears of dogs!
how you have changed

His full name was Mohandas Karamchand Gandhi, or Mohan for short. He wasn't non-violent from birth!

When asked what attribute he most admired in human nature, Mahatma Gandhi replied, simply and immediately, "Courage." "Non-violence," he said, "is not to be used ever as the shield of the coward. It is the weapon of the brave."

Richard Attenborough

faic
níl sí ag súil le faic...
an bhó

nothing
she expects nothing...
the cow

The Irish for a cow is bó and the Sanskrit is go. The river Boyne (Bóinn) is derived from the Irish goddess Boann, meaning 'white cow'. The Celtic name Bovinda (White Cow) is the same as Govinda, another name for the Indian deity Krishna. A little clue to the cradle of Indo-European civilisation! (We know about linguistic and cultural comparisons between ancient Ireland and India thanks to the work of such scholars as Myles Dillon and Franz Bopp).

bhfuil dóthain hataí ann
do gach duine...
ainniseoirí an tsaoil seo

are there hats enough
to go round...
the wretched of the earth

❗ Haiku often echo other literary works, a technique known in Japanese as *honki-dori*. Here we have an echo of a book by Frantz Fanon, *The Wretched of the Earth/Les Damnés de la Terre* (1961), an influential work which explores the dehumanising effects of colonialism.

Did Gandhi exploit the religious feelings of the Indian masses or did they see their beliefs embodied in him?

Gandhi's favourite *bhajan* (devotional song) defines what a true worshiper is. It starts like this:

> *Vaishnava jana to tene kahiye je*
> *Peed parayi jaane re*

> You are called a true worshiper
> When you can feel the pain of others

You can hear this *bhajan* on YouTube, composed by Narsinh Mehta, a fifteenth century poet-saint from Gujarat.

tá gach ní faoin spéir
faoi léas do ghrá...
stumpaí lobhair

all of creation
is bathed in your love...
a leper's stumps

According to economist Utsa Patnaik, Britain extracted $45 trillion from India during the period 1769 -1938. Imagine how that money might have been spent for the benefit of the people of India.*

Many admirers of Gandhi – friends and fellow-workers – were thrown into jail for their beliefs and activities, including a remarkable Irish woman Margaret Cousins, founder of the Women's Indian Association in 1917.

"Is there any man or woman here tonight or anywhere in the wide world who really believes that it is in order to benefit the people of India that Britain insists on holding India against the Indian people's will? Do you think it is because the British really think they can govern the people of India better than the people of India can govern themselves? Do you think they keep on in India because they want to improve the conditions of the Indians, morally or materially?... The imperial motive is greed."

Éamon de Valera †

* Source: *Agrarian and Other Histories, Essays for Binay Bhushan Chaudhuri,* edited by Shubhra Chakrabarti and Utsa Patnaik, Tulika Books

† Source: *India and Ireland,* Friends of Freedom for India, New York, 1920

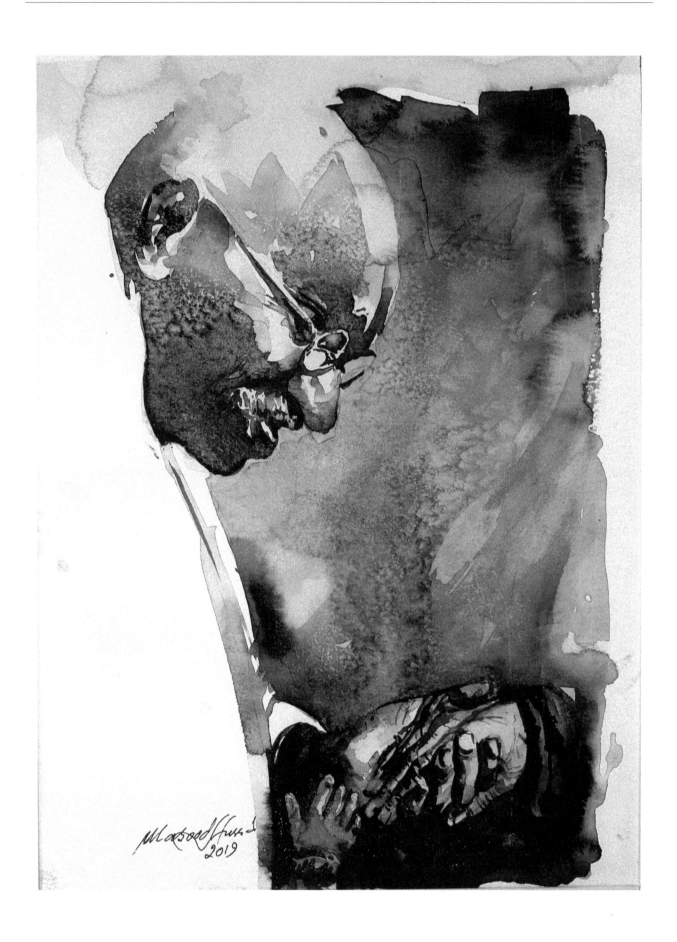

lámh ar nós
lámh ar bith eile...
an t-aos seachanta

a hand
like any other hand...
the untouchables

If you belonged to the bottom rung on the ladder of Indian society, you were Untouchable. Someone from the highest ranks of society feels polluted if even a shadow of an
Untouchable falls on them. The Untouchables are known as Dalits today, from the Sanskrit word dal, to crush or separate, related to the Irish verb dealaigh, 'separate'.

Not everyone believes that Gandhi did enough to question or dismantle the ancient
hierarchical structures of Hindu society. Today, many Dalits convert to Islam, Buddhism
or Christianity as a form of protest against this rigid system.

Of course, many societies have their own forms of class discrimination, snobbishness
and exclusiveness, often based on dress, accent, schooling, money, property and other
outer distinctive markings; others have secret codes through which they identify themselves to one another through membership of private clubs, etc.

d'ithis tráth feoil ghabhair
ach chualaís ag meigeallach í...
id' bholg istigh!

you once ate goat meat
but heard it bleating...
in your insides!

!
Bizarre, but true!
Do you like the artwork by Masood Hussain? Pick a few of your favourite haiku from this book and illustrate them in your own style.

You might like to investigate *haiga* which is a specific art form combining haiku and illustration. You could make a small greeting card, or something bigger, a calendar, a poster, for instance – or even bigger still, a mural!

Let's take a short break from haiku. Here are some sayings of Gandhi. Are there one or two of these sayings that resonate deeply with you? Is there one or more of these sayings with which you disagree? Why? (You may disagree with Gandhi – but, if possible, do not disagree violently!)

The moment the slave resolves that he will no longer be a slave, his fetters fall. He frees himself and shows the way to others. Freedom and slavery are mental states.

Truth resides in every human heart, and one has to search for it there, and to be guided by truth as one sees it. But no one has a right to coerce others to act according to his own view of truth.

An eye for an eye will only make the whole world blind.

I call him religious who understands the suffering of others.

Poverty is the worst form of violence.

There are many causes I would die for. There is not a single cause I would kill for.

You assist an administration most effectively by obeying its orders and decrees. An evil administration never deserves such allegiance.

A free India will throw all her weight in favour of world disarmament and should herself be prepared to give a lead in this.

My plea is for banishing the English language as a cultural usurper, as we successfully banished the political rule of the English usurper.

The best way to find yourself is to lose yourself in the service of others.

You must not lose faith in humanity. Humanity is like an ocean; if a few drops of the ocean are dirty, the ocean does not become dirty.

A 'No' uttered from the deepest conviction is better than a 'Yes' merely uttered to please, or worse, to avoid trouble.

The day the power of love overrules the love of power, the world will know peace.

Live as if you were to die tomorrow. Learn as if you were to live forever.

Earth provides enough to satisfy every man's needs, but not every man's greed.

gach éan á rá
ina ghuth féinig
...saoirse

birds of the air
each in its own voice sings it
...freedom

Some birds are symbols of peace, such as the dove. Others represent freedom. A bird in flight is free; it doesn't recognise the borders and barriers we have created on earth.

If you like birds, do some research on the symbolism of birds. It's fascinating.

Did Gandhi like birds? Of course. After all, he was a bit of a jailbird himself! And he was flung into jail for no other reason than his desire for freedom.

A contemporary of Gandhi, the great poet Iqbal, now revered as the spiritual father of Pakistan, wrote:

In servitude life is reduced to a tiny stream, In freedom it is like the boundless ocean...

A India!
bí ar son na fírinne, na saoirse...
gach ní án

India!
stand for truth, for freedom
the highest things in life!

Here we see Gandhiji with another great contemporary, Rabindranath Tagore, poet, painter, playwright, short story writer, educationist and novelist who was awarded the Nobel Prize for Literature. This haiku echoes the vision which Tagore had for his country. (The suffix, *ji*, after Gandhi's name is a term of respect).

Towards the end of his life, Gandhi drew solace from a song that Tagore had composed:

*I believe in walking alone. I came alone in this world, I have walked alone in the valley of the shadow of death, and I shall quit alone, when the time comes.**

* Quoted in *Great Soul* by Joseph Lelyveld, Knopf, 2011

Namaste!

Gandhi's mother was very devout. Most people have one religion – or none – as an early influence in their lives but Gandhi's father enjoyed religious discussions and had people in his house who would discuss a variety of religious experience, including Hinduism, Islam, Jainism, Christianity and Zoroastrianism.

Fundamentally, all religions are the same. If someone says *Namaste* to you it means, 'I bow to the divine that is within you and within all of us.'

Strangely enough, it was while he was in London that Gandhi began to take a deep interest in his own religion. There he met such people as the Anglo-Irish activist Annie Besant who would be remembered later not only as a champion of Indian and Irish freedom but also as a Theosophist, someone with an interest in the timeless truths of all religions.

Among the pictures on the walls of his South African law office was a picture of Jesus and a picture of Annie Besant.

Later, Besant would oppose Gandhi's ideas, believing them to be unrealistic. Gandhi's mass movement could only lead to violence and chaos, she believed; the non-resistance showed by the brave men and women in Dandi was inspiring, to be sure, but could never be replicated nationally on a grand scale. She was proven to be correct.

pléascann siad fós
na hurchair úd, Bapuji...
pléascann siad fós

they still ring out
those three shots, Bapuji...
they still ring out

! *Bapu* means 'father' in many Indian languages, including Gandhi's native language,
Gujarati.

 **No living man has, either by precept or example, influenced so vast a number
of people in so direct and profound a way.**

Harold Laski

an maitheann tú dod' dhúnmharfóir é...
id' chroí istigh
an aontaíonn tú leis?

do you forgive your assassin...
and in your heart of hearts
agree with him?

Towards the end of his fruitful life, Gandhi began to doubt his own usefulness.
Was anyone listening to him anymore? Is anyone listening to him today?

He tried to heal divisions but may have created divisions as well. Today, in India, some people regard Godse, his assassin, as a patriot!

Gandhi once said, 'The weak can never forgive. Forgiveness is the attribute of the strong.'
How true is that?

an domhan ba léir duit
ag éag anois
...drúcht ceobhránach

the world you saw
is fading now
...foggy dew

! This haiku echoes an Irish folksong, *The Foggy Dew,* written in turbulent times when a
great number of men from Ireland and an even greater number from India were fighting
in the First World War on the side of the British at a time when freedom movements, of
varying shades, were gathering momentum at home; indeed, Irish and Indian intellectuals
drew strength and inspiration from each other's fight for political and cultural independence.

Pearse corresponded with Tagore whose play, *The Post Office,* had its world premiere in
Dublin. Originally written in Bengali as *Dakghar,* the English-language translation was
performed in the Abbey Theatre on May 17, 1913.

cad iad na tuaiplisí
atá déanta acu...
éiníní ar chraobh

what errors...
have they made in life...
birds on a branch

 Not since Buddha has India so revered any man... Not since St. Francis of Assisi has any life known to history been so marked by gentleness, disinterestedness, simplicity of soul, and forgiveness of enemies... We have the astonishing phenomenon of a revolution led by a saint.
Will Durant

cuaráin Gandhi...
cad a thairgfear dom...
an gcloisim $10,000

Gandhi's sandals...
what am I bid...
do I hear $10,000

! The commodification of everything today would horrify Gandhi. Must everything have a price? How would you feel if mankind decided to phase out money altogether and instead of money we had a gift economy, that is to say a free exchange of products and services?

Decentralisation in economics must go hand in hand with decentralisation in politics. Individuals, families and small co-operative groups should own the land and instruments necessary for their own subsistence and for supplying a local market. Among these necessary instruments of production Gandhi wished to include only hand tools...
Aldous Huxley in Visva-Bharati Quarterly, October 2 1949

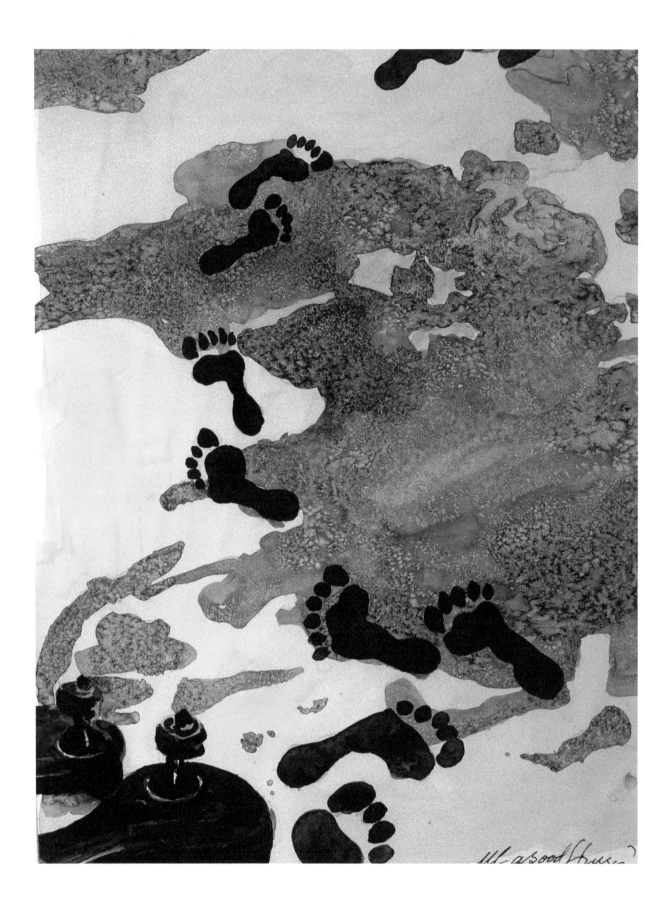

Bapu! lorg do choise ar fud na bhfud...
cé leanfaidh anois thú
cé

Bapu! your footprint everywhere...
who can follow you now
who

Even harsh critics of Gandhi, such as Arundhati Roy, admit that the Salt March was brilliant political theatre. 60,000 followed Gandhi on that great march. How many believe in his message today? How many are brave enough to practice civil disobedience in the face of injustice?

It was while he was imprisoned in Johannesburg that he first read Henry David Thoreau's essay, *Civil Disobedience*.

"It impressed him deeply. Thoreau had gone to jail for refusing to pay taxes that would help fund US aggression against Mexico. It was not enough to say you oppose evil, wrote Thoreau: you must take action." *

* *Mahatma Gandhi, Nonviolent Liberator* by Richard L. Deats, Mary Jegen, New City Press, 2005

loitiméirí
níor thángadar ar do chroí
...dealbh gan chloigeann

vandals
they couldn't find your heart
...beheaded statue

The above lines faintly echo a famous Japanese haiku by an eccentric hermit, Ryōkan. There are some things beyond the reach of thieves!

the thief left it behind...
the moon
at my window

Críostaí, Giúdach,
Hiondúch, Mahamadach
...níl reiligiún ar bith ag Dia

Christian, Jew,
Hindu, Mohammedan
...God has no religion

Gandhi's statement, 'God has no religion' is the perfect retort to fundamentalists who assert that their religion and only theirs is the true one. Gandhi echoes the insights of a medieval weaver and poet-saint, Kabir:
I am neither in temple nor in mosque
I am neither at Kaaba nor at Kailash
Neither am I in rites and ceremonies
Nor Yoga nor in renunciation...

Denis Hurley, Catholic Archbishop of Durban in South Africa said:
The great religions of the world will have to work together. They will all be sitting at Gandhi's feet...

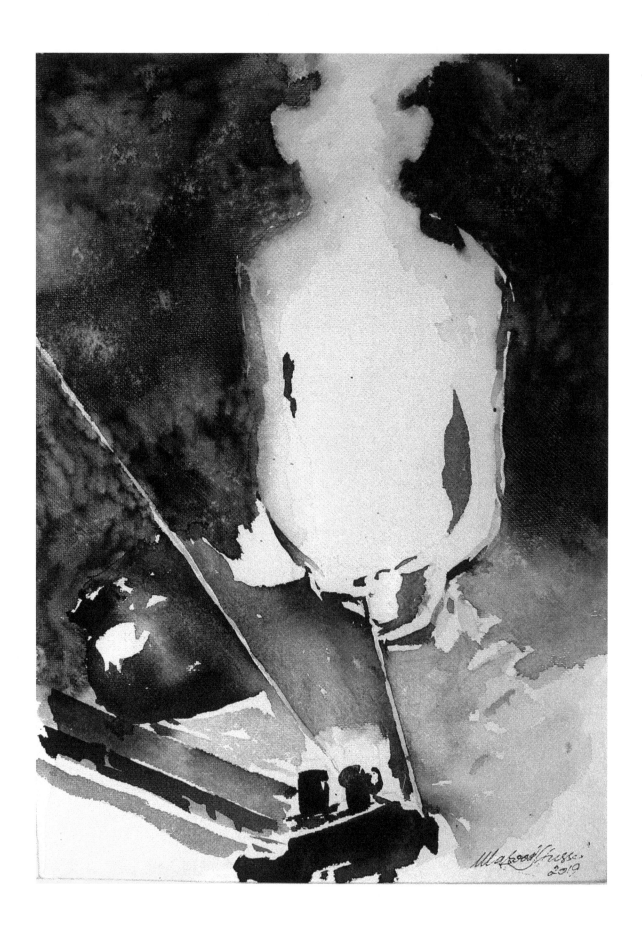

ní chloiseann ár gcroí é
a thuilleadh...
an tuirne

our hearts
no longer hear it...
spinning wheel

Ah, the spinning wheel! A symbol of traditional self-sufficiency. Spinning was a ritual for Gandhi and he often made his own clothes while in prison, encouraging others to do the same and not rely on clothes imported from Britain.

In his final years, he and his followers began the day with spinning – at four o'clock in the morning! Spinning was a form of meditation: Gandhi disliked the way the slow rhythms of work which we knew for thousands of years were disrupted by the so-called advances of modern technology.

Was he right? Or is this what is called hypophysics? Hypophysics means everything that is natural is valuable in itself and what is unnatural must be avoided. Wear natural clothes, eat natural foods and so on. That's fine.

But is it natural to take a flight from Dublin to Delhi?

Is it natural to undergo a heart transplant?

Was Gandhi a Luddite? The original Luddites smashed machinery because it was replacing traditional arts and crafts.

If he were alive today, would Gandhi favour Neo-Luddism, or Anarcho-Primitivism, a return to nature, a rejection of unbridled technology?

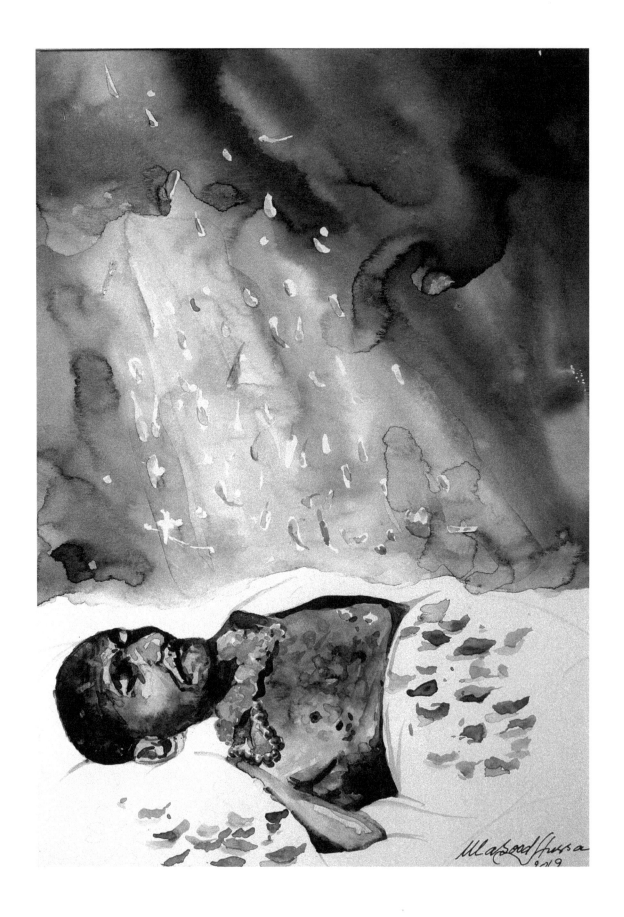

tit go séimh
séimh ar a chorp...
peitil ó neamh

*fall gently
gently on his corpse...
petals from heaven*

It wasn't a man called Godse who killed Gandhi. No, no, no! Not at all. According to a wise Indian philosopher, Jiddu Krishnamurti, you killed him. I'm afraid so. Yes, you! You held the Beretta 9mm pistol in your hand and shot him three times. I killed him as well. We all killed him. As long as we see ourselves as divided, one from the other, we are potentially very dangerous – deadly in fact.

In the course of a public talk in Mumbai, shortly after Gandhiji's death, Krishnamurti tried to get this point across, reminding us of the fractured nature of humanity, our blindness to the oneness and sacredness of us all. If you want a name for this philosophy, it's *Advaita* or Non-duality. He said:

You are either a Hindu, a Parsee, a Buddhist, or a Mussulman – you know, the whole rot of identified division, isolation. So... you are responsible, aren't you? You are the real cause of this murder.

This is classic Indian philosophy and it's what Gandhi himself believed, seeing the Self in all and all in the Self.

breocharn...
dúinn go léir í
tine seo na híobartha

funeral pyre...
this sacrifice burns
for us all

Regarded simply as a politician, and compared with the other leading political figures of our time, how clean a smell he has managed to leave behind!

George Orwell

ó, a Abhainn Yamuna
thugais leat a luaithreach...
cén áit cén áit?

oh Yamuna River
you have taken his ashes...
where oh where?

One of Gandhi's biographers, Stanley Wolpert, gives us a stirring summary of the Mahatma's true nature and achievement:

By re-creating himself, through the power of his passion, in the humble, vulnerable, image of India's poorest starving naked millions, Gandhi could... call upon that unarmed ragged army, whose pain he mirrored and magnified in his own naked body, to follow him barefoot.

Mahatma: The Early Years

Gandhi is born in Porbandar, a coastal town in Gujarat, India, on October 2 1869. He attends primary school in 1876. Ancient Indian epics light up his imagination. Slight of stature, Gandhi is quite a nervous boy and hasn't much aptitude for sports or studies. Does it matter? Not at all. It's who you are in your heart and soul that really matters!

Gandhi finds Truth and Courage in the old epics, just as many Irish people derive inspiration from the beautiful poems and heroic tales of the Fiannaíocht: *glaine ár gcroí*/purity of heart/*neart ár ngéag*/strength of limb/*is beart de réir ár mbriathar*/action to match our words.

(This was the mantra, by the way, on a banner in the home of the revolutionary Countess Markievicz; her home was looted by British soldiers and the banner, seen as a war trophy, is now housed in the Imperial War Museum in London).

Back to Gandhi!

By 1881 he's in secondary school and still no wiser.

In 1883, at the age of thirteen, he marries 14-year-old Kasturbai Makhanji ("Ba" for short). He's still a fearful teenager and sleeps with the light on. But he is also entering the rebellious stage of youth and with every misdeed, he promises to himself, 'Never again!'

His father dies in 1885 and a first child is born to the young couple, Kasturbai and Mohandas Gandhi. The child dies after a few days. The couple have four more children, all sons.

On September 4 1888, he goes to London to train as a barrister. He wants to fit in, to become an English gentleman, and so he gets elocution lessons!

In London, he meets Theosophists, people searching for the truth behind all religions and his interest in his own religion, Hinduism, is ignited.

Jainism was a religion which was strong in his home area of Western India and when he reads the New Testament and the teachings of Christ, he is struck by the similarity between what Christ taught and the teachings of the founder of Jainism, Mahavira, who said:
In happiness and suffering, in joy and grief, we should regard all creatures as we regard our own self.

While in London, his political consciousness began to form as well:
...he came in touch with liberal and Christian ideas and the then novel teachings of Tolstoy about non-cooperation with evil and violence.
Freedom Fighters of India, M. G. Agrawal (Gyan Publishing House, 2008)

June 12, 1891, the qualified barrister arrives in Bombay (Mumbai today) and hears the very sad news that his mother has passed away.

He cannot find his feet as a lawyer and accepts a job in Natal, South Africa, then part of the British Empire. Insult after insult await him there. In a Durban courthouse, a magistrate orders him to remove his turban. He is ejected from a "whites only" carriage in a train; refused entry in hotels; endures the violent language and behaviour of the ruling classes.

Let us be forever grateful to the oaf who threw Gandhi off the train in Maritzburg where he spent the night in a cold waiting-room. He has had enough! He emerges as a fighter – a fighter the likes we have never known before, armed only with truth, love, courage and humility. These qualities are in all of us, waiting to be born!

What happens to him next? Try the library!

Wherever war and destruction occur today, whenever bullies, oafs and populists start flexing their muscles, we can evoke the spirit of the Mahatma and find our own path of dignified protest and civil disobedience.

tost i lár na bhfothrach
...glórbhosca na bábóige
briste

silence amid ruins
...a doll's voice box
broken

The creators of this book

Masood Hussain, an accomplished draughtsman and prolific watercolorist, honed his formidable skills at Sir J.J. Institute of Applied Arts, Mumbai. Masood teaches at the Institute of Music & Fine Arts in Srinagar, Kashmir, where he was born and raised. "The Vale of Kashmir draws us to imagine ourselves," Masood says, "amidst her lush shades of green, crystal clear lakes, gushing streams, snow-capped peaks — a paradise that has sadly been in pathos now for over a generation. We need a Gandhi to sort us out."

Gabriel Rosenstock is a bilingual poet (in Irish & English), haikuist, tankaist, playwright, novelist, short story writer, essayist, translator, writer for children and champion of 'forlorn causes' – the phrase is Hugh MacDiarmid's. He is a Lineage Holder of Celtic Buddhism and a member of Aosdána (the Irish academy of arts and letters). Among his awards is the *Tamgha-i-Khidmat* medal (Pakistan) for services to literature. Gabriel's most recent volume of poetry is *Glengower: Poems for No One in Irish and English* (The Onslaught Press).

Writers'
Garage

SERVICES AND RESOURCES FOR INDEPENDENT WRITERS

CPSIA information can be obtained
at www.ICGtesting.com
Printed in the USA
BVHW021658260919
559532BV00015B/212/P

9 781916 225404